COLLECTION EDITOR **JENNIFER GRÜNWALD**
ASSISTANT EDITOR **CAITLIN O'CONNELL**
ASSOCIATE MANAGING EDITOR **KATERI WOODY**
EDITOR, SPECIAL PROJECTS **MARK D. BEAZLEY**

VP PRODUCTION & SPECIAL PROJECTS **JEFF YOUNGQUIST**
SVP PRINT, SALES & MARKETING **DAVID GABRIEL**
BOOK DESIGNER **ADAM DEL RE**

EDITOR IN CHIEF **AXEL ALONSO**
CHIEF CREATIVE OFFICER **JOE QUESADA**
PRESIDENT **DAN BUCKLEY**
EXECUTIVE PRODUCER **ALAN FINE**

THE TOTALLY AWESOME HULK

BIG APPLE SHOWDOWN

GREG PAK
WRITER

ISSUE NOS. 13-14

LUKE ROSS (#13) &
GERMÁN PERALTA (#13-14)
ARTISTS

JAY DAVID RAMOS &
DONO SÁNCHEZ-ALMARA
COLORISTS

BERNARD CHANG &
MARCELO MAIOLO
COVER ART

ISSUE NOS. 15-18

MAHMUD ASRAR
ARTIST

NOLAN WOODARD
COLORIST

STONEHOUSE
COVER ART

VC's CORY PETIT
LETTERER

CHRIS ROBINSON
ASSISTANT EDITOR

MARK PANICCIA
EDITOR

HULK CREATED BY **STAN LEE** & **JACK KIRBY**

HI! I'M MADDY CHO, SISTER OF SUPER-GENIUS TEENAGER **AMADEUS CHO**. WELL, *THIS* ISN'T ME...I'M ACTUALLY... NEVER MIND, YOU'LL SEE.

ANYWAY, MONTHS AGO, OFF THE KENYAN COAST, AN EXPERIMENTAL FUSION REACTOR HAD FAILED AND THREATENED THE LIVES OF FIFTY MILLION PEOPLE. **BRUCE BANNER**, AS THE **HULK**, STOPPED THE MELTDOWN BY PHYSICALLY ABSORBING THE RADIATION. ALTHOUGH HE WAS ABLE TO STOP THE THREAT, THE HULK'S PHYSIOLOGY COULDN'T HANDLE ALL THAT ENERGY, AND HE CAME CLOSE TO A MELTDOWN OF HIS OWN.

AMADEUS ARRIVED AND, AGAINST TONY STARK'S ORDERS, ABSORBED ALL OF BRUCE'S RADIATION. AS A RESULT, AMADEUS IS NOW

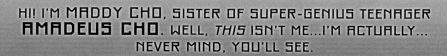

THE TOTALLY AWESOME HULK

NOW, AFTER STOPPING A MONSTER ATTACK IN AUSTIN, TEXAS, AMADEUS IS LOOKING TO UNWIND...

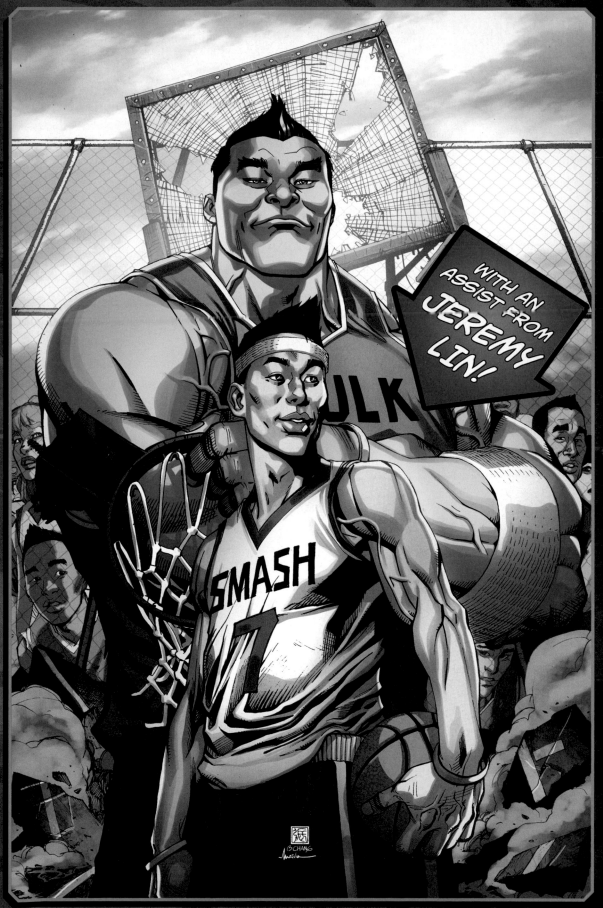

OLYMPUS GROUP SECRET HQ ATX001, TWO MILES NORTH OF TOWN.

WHAAAAAT?!

I KNOW, RIGHT?

YOU CHILL, I'LL GET SOME FOOD.

MADDY, MADDY, MADDY, MADDY YOU GOTTA CALL ME, *JEREMY LIN'S* CHILLING OVER HERE, YOU GOTTA COME OVER MADDY!

MADDY?

TCH.

HNH.

AH. JUST LIKE THE GOOD OL' DAYS.

DUDE, I'M TELLING YOU, YOU CAN HAVE THE BED!

NAH, THE COUCH IS COOL. GOTTA STAY HUMBLE.

ALL RIGHT, THEN. SLEEP TIGHT!

YO, AMADEUS.

WHAT?

IF YOU'RE NOT DOING ANYTHING, YOU SHOULD COME TO MY *EVENT* TOMORROW.

REALLY?

YEAH, IT'S A CHARITY BASKETBALL THING.

I'LL TELL 'EM TO GET A JERSEY FOR YA.

WAIT, WHAT? YOU WANT ME TO *PLAY*?

YEAH, YOU CAN SHOW OFF THAT THREE!

COOL.

TAK TAK TAK TAK TAKETY TAK

MADDY OMG I'M GONNA PLAY BASKETBALL WITH JLIN7 TOMORROW YOU GOTTA COME THIS IS NUTS!!!!!

MADDY U THERE?

MADDY?

HMPH.

KTHOOOOM

DID YOU SEE THAT? IT JUST--

TELEPORTED.

YEAH. BUT DON'T WORRY. IT DROPPED SOME *DEBRIS*--

--WHICH IS ALL I NEED...

BLEEP

SCANNING CODE...

...MATCH.

DANG IT.

WHAT?

THE DRAGON'S *CHIPS* ARE DRIVEN BY *MY CODE.*

YOU MEAN FROM THAT *GAME* YOU SHOWED ME?

YEAH. WHATEVER WAS TRYING TO *HACK* ME FINALLY *DID.*

OLYMPUS GROUP AIR COMMAND! THIS IS *DIRECTOR CHO!*

I'M UPLOADING A TRACKING SIGNATURE...

YOU'VE GOT AN AIR FORCE?

OKAY. COOL.

I NEED YOU TO SCRAMBLE ALL JETS IN NORTH AND CENTRAL AMERICAN AIRSPACE!

THAT WOULD BE A *NEGATIVE,* AMADEUS.

WHAT?

KTHOOOP

OW!
WHAT THE HECK--

HEY! WHAT?
TEMPORARY GAMMA INHIBITOR.

YOU'RE NOT THE ONLY GENIUS IN THE FAMILY, DUDE.

NICE TO MEET YOU, JEREMY.

UH. YEAH. LIKEWISE.

YOU'RE NOT GETTING RID OF ME LIKE THAT, MADDY!

I GOT A JOB TO DO AND I'M DOING IT!

ME, TOO. CAN YOU TRACK HER?

WAIT, JEREMY, THIS HAS GOTTEN TOO CRAZY. YOU JUST CHILL HERE AND--

NO WAY, DUDE. I'M COMING WITH YOU. ARCH-E'S A FELLOW PLAYER. I'M NOT BAILING WHILE HE'S IN TROUBLE.

BUT--

AND I FIGURE SOMEONE'S GOTTA KEEP AN EYE ON YOU.

COME ON--

AND MY CAR'S PARKED THREE BLOCKS AWAY.

HM.

15

AW, CRAP, I'M ON MY WAY.

YOU'RE LATE!

I KNOW, I KNOW! JUST SAVING THE WORLD AND—

COME ON!

OLYMPUS GROUP RESTRAINING TITAN-O-FOAM.

FFFSSSSST

GLAAARG!

SORRY, PHALKAN. I'VE GOT A PRIOR ENGAGEMENT.

BUT I'M SURE ALPHA FLIGHT'LL LET YOU CALL YOUR PLANET FOR BAIL MONEY AND LEGAL REPRESENTATION BEFORE THEY LOCK YOU UP—

—'CAUSE THAT'S THE WAY WE ROOOOLLLLL!

AMADEUS!

TWO SECONDS!

WE'RE OUT OF TIME!

FLUSHING, QUEENS.

AND I'M HERE!

WHOOOOOOM

LET'S GO LET'S GO LET'S GO LET'S GO!

DUDE, YOU SHOULD TRY SOME COMMAS SOMETIME.

JAKE OH, AGENT OF S.H.I.E.L.D.

THOSE KIDS, MAN. KILLING ME.

OH MY GOD, THOSE COSTUMES!

I NEARLY CRIED, I SWEAR TO GOD.

THE HULK, A.K.A. AMADEUS CHO, IN HIS PUNY HUMAN FORM.

YEAH. YOU'VE GOT A LOT OF PEOPLE LOOKING UP TO YOU.

ALL THOSE SECOND AND THIRD GENERATION KIDS...

...WHEN HAVE THEY EVER SEEN PEOPLE WHO LOOK AND SOUND LIKE THEM DOING WHAT YOU DO?

I KNOW YOU *THINK* YOU'RE A PRETTY *BIG DEAL.*

BUT THE CRAZY THING IS, YOU ACTUALLY *ARE.*

SO DON'T SCREW IT UP.

HEY, WHY'S EVERYONE LOOKING AT ME?

HA!

WHATEVER.

LET'S GET OUR *KALBI* ON!

YUSS!

WHAT'S KALBI?

KOREAN BARBECUE. *BEEF!*

YOU COOK IT AT THE TABLE, WRAP IT IN LETTUCE. IT'S THE BEST.

OH, WAIT, SORRY, DO YOU EAT BEEF?

YEAH, I'M MUSLIM, NOT HINDU.

OH, SHOOT. I'M SORRY.

OH, NO, IT'S FINE.

AND SOME HINDUS EAT IT, TOO. I'M NOT A BIG EXPERT ON THE WHOLE THING. IT'S KIND OF COMPLICATED.

MOST THINGS ARE, HUH?

SO THE KALBI'S DONE FAMILY-STYLE, BUT THERE ARE OTHER OPTIONS, TOO. I'M GONNA JUST GET BIBIMBAP.

WHAT? REALLY?

I'M VEGETARIAN.

REALLY?

BUT...YOU'RE *KOREAN.*

YEP.

KALBI, DUDE.

COMPLICATED, DUDE.

AMADEUS, SERIOUSLY, CAN YOU STOP BEING A JERK FOR TWO SECONDS?

OKAY, OKAY...

...FOR THE KIDS.

THAT'S RIGHT. FOR THE KIDS.

...MY PARENTS *HATED* IT WHEN I WENT INTO *ESPIONAGE.* THEY WANTED ME TO BE A *DOCTOR.*

SAME.

EXCEPT MY PARENTS WANTED ME TO BE A *LAWYER.*

A LAWYER? REALLY?

YEAH.

MY DAD'S RIDICULOUS. I LOVE HIM. BUT HE'S SO *PARANOID* ABOUT EVERYTHING. LIKE, HE'S NEVER BROKEN A LAW IN HIS *LIFE,* BUT HE ALWAYS THINKS HE'S GONNA GET *BLAMED* FOR SOMETHING.

NOW HE'S THINKING I SHOULD *MARRY* A LAWYER.

NO, WAIT.

A *KOREAN* GIRL WHO'S ALSO A *METHODIST* AND A LAWYER.

AND A *CORPORATE* LAWYER. NOT A PUBLIC DEFENDER.

BUT SHE SHOULD HAVE *GOOD FRIENDS* IN THE D.A.'S OFFICE. JUST IN CASE.

YES, HE HAS.

HE'S REALLY THOUGHT THIS THROUGH.

SO...WHO *ARE* YOU DATING?

A METHODIST CORPORATE LAWYER.

WHO'S ALSO A BLACK DUDE.

FOR REAL?

YEP.

HA, HA!

DAP

ONE THING ABOUT YOUR FATHER...

...HE WANTS YOU TO BE *SAFE.* WHICH IS WHAT EVERYONE WANTS FOR THEIR FAMILY.

OH, MAN, JIMMY, I KNOW YOU'RE LIKE *EIGHTY* OR WHATEVER, BUT DON'T RUIN THE *VIBE* AND SAY SOMETHING--

LET ME FINISH.

THIS IS WHY I'M SO PROUD OF ALL OF YOU.

YOU'RE ALL SO *DIFFERENT* FROM THE WORLD AROUND YOU. EVEN FROM EACH OTHER.

AND YET YOU CHOSE TO STICK *OUT...*

...TO MAKE YOURSELVES *UNSAFE...*

...IN ORDER TO STICK *UP* FOR OTHERS.

FOR *EVERYBODY.*

YES. AND THAT'S WHAT MAKES YOU HEROES.

GOD BLESS YOU ALL.

TOO LATE, BRO.

MAD ASIAN-DAD ACTION UP IN THIS PIECE.

WORD.

FINE.

YOU PAY FOR *DINNER,* AMADEUS CHO...

...BUT *I'M* PAYING FOR KARAOKE.

YUSSS!

THE THING I NEVER GOT WAS "OLIVE-SKINNED."

COME ON, MAN. OLIVES ARE *GREEN*.

SO'S THE HULK.

HA HA HA HA!

CRAP, YOU MEAN I CAN'T COMPLAIN ABOUT THAT ONE ANY-MORE?

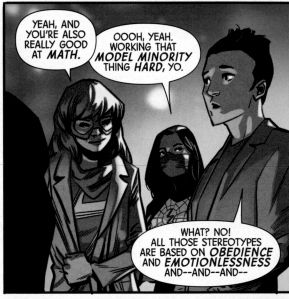

YEAH, AND YOU'RE ALSO REALLY GOOD AT *MATH*.

OOOH, YEAH. WORKING THAT *MODEL MINORITY* THING *HARD*, YO.

WHAT? NO! ALL THOSE STEREOTYPES ARE BASED ON *OBEDIENCE* AND *EMOTIONLESSNESS* AND--AND--AND--

ASK JAKE! I'VE GOT NO *IMPULSE CONTROL*! I'M THE *OPPOSITE* OF "INSCRUTABLE"!

OKAY. I'LL GIVE YOU THAT.

YOU'RE ACTUALLY LIKE THE *MOST SCRUTABLE* PERSON I'VE EVER MET IN MY LIFE.

OKAY, WELL, THANKS, BUT THAT MIGHT BE A BIT OF AN EXAGGERATION--

SERIOUSLY. WHATEVER YOU'RE THINKING, IT'S RIGHT THERE ON YOUR FACE.

DUDE, YOU HAVE ALL THOSE *S.H.I.E.L.D. BIOMETRIC READERS* AND WHATNOT.

OF COURSE *YOU* CAN TELL WHAT I'M--

16

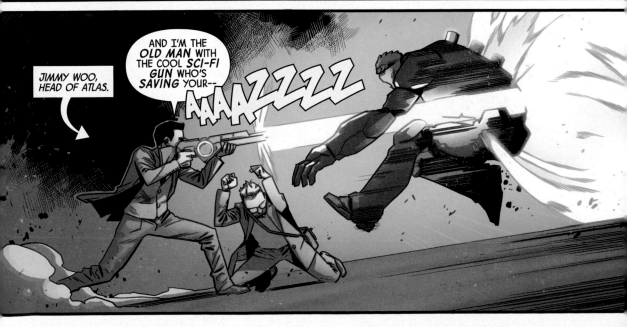

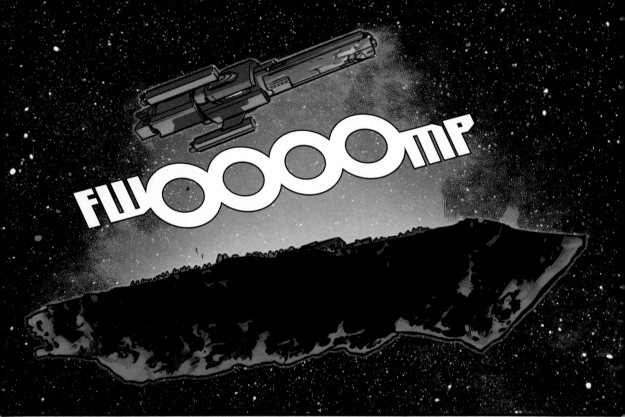

AW, CRAP.

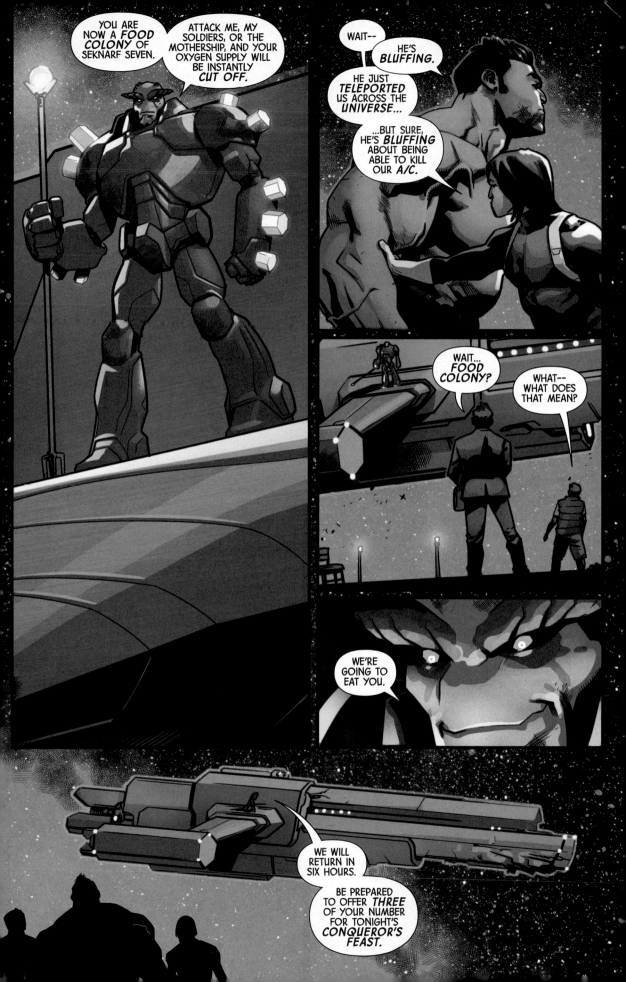

OFFICER, HOW ABOUT A HEAD COUNT? SEE WHO NEEDS ANY IMMEDIATE FIRST AID, FIND ANY DOCTORS...

RIGHT, GOOD. AND WE NEED TO RIG SOME SHELTER...

...ROUND UP FOOD AND WATER. SEE WHO CAN WATCH THE KIDS...

ALL RIGHT, FOLKS, LISTEN UP!

WE'RE ALL GONNA WORK TOGETHER, HERE.

ANY DOCTORS, NURSES, TEACHERS?

AND HOW 'BOUT ANY ENGINEERS OR ELECTRICIANS?

IBEW LOCAL #3.

AND I'M A MECHANIC, IF THAT HELPS.

HECK YEAH.

WHAT'S THE PLAN?

I'M GUESSING THESE *SPEARS* ARE GENERATING THE GRAVITY AND ATMOSPHERE.

I'M GONNA FIGURE OUT HOW THEY WORK.

AND WE'RE GONNA TAKE 'EM OVER.

AAAAAAH!

17

OKAY, LET'S THINK ABOUT THAT.

THAT *ENERGY DOME* HAS DISABLED OUR *ELECTRONICS* AND DISRUPTED YOUR ABILITY TO TRANSFORM INTO THE *HULK.*

BUT *SILK, SHANG-CHI,* AND *MS. MARVEL* STILL HAVE THEIR POWERS.

THAT'S RIGHT...

HECK YEAH!

...AND WE'RE GONNA WATCH OUT FOR EVERYONE HERE.

'CAUSE WE'RE THE *PROTECTORS,* OKAY?

O-OKAY.

ALL RIGHT, MY *BRAIN'S* STILL WORKING, SO HERE'S EVERYTHING I'VE FIGURED OUT ABOUT THEIR *TECHNOLOGY.*

I'M LOOKING AT *THREE KEY VULNERABILITIES*--

WAIT, WAIT, WAIT...

...DIDN'T THAT *ALIEN PRINCE* SAY HE'D CUT OFF OUR *OXYGEN* IF WE FIGHT?

JEFFREY GUNDERSON, ASSISTANT ACCOUNT EXECUTIVE, OLYMPIBANK, EIGHTH AVENUE BRANCH.

HE SURE DID.

HE ALSO SAID HE'D *EAT* US, JEFFREY.

YOU CAN'T TAKE EVERYTHING EVERYONE SAYS *LITERALLY.*

HE SAID WE WERE A *FOOD COLONY!*

WELL, ENGLISH MAY NOT BE HIS *FIRST LANGUAGE,* SO--

DID YOU SEE HIS TEETH?

I'M JUST SAYING...

LOOK, IF ANYONE WANTS TO OPT OUT OF FIGHTING FOR YOUR *LIVES* AGAINST THE ALIEN *HUMANIVORES,* LINE UP OVER HERE AND I'LL WRITE YOU NOTES ABSOLVING YOU OF ANY *RESPONSIBILITY.*

NO? OKAY. GOOD.

WAIT.

AMADEUS DID A GOOD JOB OF SETTING THAT UP SO HE'D ONLY GET *ONE* ANSWER.

BUT LET'S JUST ALL MAKE SURE WE KNOW WHAT'S HAPPENING HERE.

LOOKING GOOD!

IT'S COMING ALONG, HUH?

YOU GUYS, THIS IS GONNA BE AAAAAWESOME!

THWIP

THWIP

HAHA!

YAAAAAA!

THANK YOU.

NO PROBLEM.

WE'RE-- WE'RE ALL DEPENDING ON YOU.

I SWEAR TO YOU.

WE'LL DIE BEFORE ANYTHING HAPPENS TO THESE KIDS.

... YOU GONNA SAY ANYTHING?

AFTER WE DID THAT BENEFIT WITH THE *KIDS* YESTERDAY, I GOT ALL *NERVOUS* WHEN YOU STARTED LECTURING *JAKE* ABOUT HIS CRAZY *DAD.*

I THOUGHT YOU WERE GONNA SAY SOMETHING *AWFUL.*

BUT INSTEAD YOU WERE *AWESOME.*

YOU *SAID* YOU WERE *PROUD* OF US. BECAUSE WE CHOSE TO *STICK OUT.*

TO MAKE OURSELVES *UNSAFE.*

IN ORDER TO STICK UP FOR *OTHERS.*

FOR *EVERYBODY.*

YOU REMEMBERED ALL THAT, WORD FOR WORD?

IT MEANT A LOT TO ME.

I STILL BELIEVE ALL OF IT.

NO. YOU *THINK* YOU DO...

...BUT YOU'VE GOT A WEIRD IDEA OF *"EVERYBODY."*

THOSE ALIENS WERE GOING TO *KILL* AND *EAT* US, AMADEUS.

GOOD JOB, DUDE.

YOU THINK SO?

STOPPING A *MASS MURDER* ALWAYS GETS A BIG *THUMBS 'UP* IN MY BOOK.

I JUST WANT *ONE CLEAN WIN.*

IS THAT TOO MUCH TO ASK?

A LITTLE *SUCCESS* WITHOUT THIS HORRIBLE *GRAY AREA, TRAGIC CRAP* TACKED ON AT THE END?

UGH. *JIMMY.* I KNOW.

YEAH.

BUT COME ON. PEOPLE YOU WANNA JUST LOVE ARE ALWAYS GONNA *DISAPPOINT.*

THAT'S JUST *LIFE.*

WE JUST GOTTA KEEP DOING WHAT WE DO.

JIMMY'S RIGHT ABOUT THAT, WHETHER HE GETS IT OR NOT.

FOR THE KIDS, RIGHT?

DEFINITELY.

HECK YEAH...

END.

13 DIVIDED WE STAND VARIANT BY **ELIZABETH TORQUE**

15 STORY THUS FAR VARIANT BY **GIUSEPPE CAMUNCOLI** & **DANIELE ORLANDINI**

15 VARIANT BY **MUKESH SINGH**

15 CLASSIC VARIANT BY **RICH BUCKLER**, **TOM PALMER** & **FRANK MARTIN**

17 VENOMIZED VARIANT BY **MIKE CHOI**